Oli the bicycle

A story about a girl born with Foetal Alcohol Syndrome

Catherine Jackson

Illustrations by Rachel Fuller

BAAF
Saffron House, 6–10 Kirby Street, London EC1N 8XS
Registered Charity No. 275689

Published by
British Association for Adoption & Fostering
(BAAF)
Saffron House
6–10 Kirby Street
London EC1N 8TS
www.baaf.org.uk

Charity registration 275689 (England and Wales)
and SC039337 (Scotland)

British Library Cataloguing in Publication Data
A catalogue record for this book is available from
the British Library

ISBN 978 1 910039 09 0

Project management by Michelle Bell, Publications
Department, BAAF
Designed and typeset by Fravashi Aga
Printed in Great Britain by the Lavenham Press
Trade distribution by Turnaround Publisher Services,
Unit 3, Olympia Trading Estate, Coburg Road, London
N22 6TZ

BAAF is the leading UK-wide membership organisation
for all those concerned with adoption, fostering and
child care issues.

The author
Catherine Jackson is a writer, journalist and cartoonist. She is the author of *Parenting a child with mental health issues* (BAAF, 2012).

The illustrator
Since graduating from Brighton Art College in 1996, Rachel Fuller has produced artwork for a range of magazines, design groups and advertising agencies. She is, however, predominantly known for her work in children's books. Rachel develops her own ideas, often in the form of novelty and interactive packages for young children. She also enjoys illustrating picture books, educational material and teen fiction. She has illustrated a number of books for BAAF, including *Morris and the bundle of worries*, *Elfa and the box of memories* and *A safe place for Rufus*.

The series editor
The editor of this series, Hedi Argent, is an established author/editor for BAAF. Her books cover a wide range of family placement topics; she has written several guides and a story book for young children.

Other books in this series

My brother Booh has ADHD – A story about a boy with Attention Deficit Hyperactivity Disorder

Sam's trouble with words – A story about a boy with dyslexia

Why can't I be good? – A story about an adopted girl with behaviour problems

This is a story about a girl called Oli who was born with Foetal Alcohol Syndrome. If you have difficulty learning new things, taking part in sports or games, or getting along with other people, among other things, you may find Oli's story helpful. Even if you can read it yourself, you may want to ask a grown-up to read the story with you.

You may find that lots of the things that happen to Oli have happened, or are happening, to you. After you have read Oli's story, you may have lots of questions about Foetal Alcohol Syndrome. There is a question and answer section at the back of this book with useful information about some of the things you may want to know about Foetal Alcohol Syndrome. Of course, if you have more questions you can ask the grown-up reading the book with you, your parent, carer, social worker or teacher.

★

Oli was six and going to be seven. It was her birthday tomorrow and her mamma and pappa had promised her a pink bicycle.

They were her new mamma and pappa because before she'd lived with her first mamma, and then some people had come and taken her to live with some other people called Jenny and George for a bit, until her new mamma and pappa came to take her to her new home. So this was her first birthday in a way because she was a brand new Oli in her new family.

Oli so wanted that bicycle. She'd watched the other kids on the block doing wheelies

★

and other stuff on their BMX bikes. She could picture herself on her new pink bike, with them standing round with their mouths dropping open, all amazed. She'd do wheelies and loop the loop. She would even fly. Well, maybe not fly.

So it was the night before her birthday and she lay curled up in bed with the covers scrunched up round her ears and she tried really really hard to go to sleep because Mamma had said, 'Now Oli, you MUST go to sleep because you need to get your beauty sleep for our shopping trip tomorrow.' 'Not,' said Pappa, picking her up and throwing her into the air, 'that Oli isn't THE most beautiful little girl in the world already.'

So Oli tried really hard to go to sleep by closing her eyes tight, but the harder she tried the more her mind went whizzing round and round and round like a bug in a jam jar. She thought about the pink bike and getting up

★

with the sun shining. She'd take her mamma and pappa a cup of tea in bed, and there would be cards in the post and presents to open, and they'd get up and have special eggy toast made by Pappa because that was his "speciality". Then they'd go to the bus stop and they'd see Mrs Samski from the next floor down and Oli would say, 'It's my birthday, Mrs Samski, and I'm seven and we're going to buy me a pink bicycle,' and Mrs Samski would smile like she always did and say, 'Is good, Oli.' Oli thought maybe Mrs Samski didn't have many words in her word book because that's what she always said. Except sometimes, when she said, 'Poor Oli. Is not good.' That was when Oli had a tantrum.

Then suddenly Oli woke up and it WAS morning and it WAS her birthday and the sun WAS shining and the whole world was all quiet, except Oli could hear a bird singing in the tree outside the flat. So she pressed her nose against the glass and whispered, 'Hello bird, it's my birthday,' and the bird, who was

★

her friend and often sang to her, sang a special
song for her birthday.

Then Oli got up very quietly and peeped
into the sitting room and there was a pile of
presents on the table and a huge card with
HAPPY BIRTHDAY OLI written in great big
pink letters. Oli so wanted to rip off all the
wrappings and find out what was
inside the parcels, but then she
remembered that in her new family
no one was going to take away her
presents, and they'd still be there if
she waited a bit. So she curled up on the
sofa in her bunny onesie, and just looked and
looked and looked at the presents that were all
her own.

Then the door opened and there was Mamma
saying, 'What time do you call this?' in a big
cross voice. But Oli knew she was only teasing
because it was her birthday, so she said,
'It's my birthday time!' and jumped into her
mamma's arms. Later, when she unwrapped

★

one of her presents, which was a great big box, she found a smaller box inside it and inside that was an even smaller box, and then lots more smaller boxes until the very final, smallest box, and when she opened that, there was a lovely pink watch that would tell her what the real time was.

After eggy breakfast, they put on their coats and went down to the bus stop to go into town to buy Oli a pink bicycle. Mrs Samski was at the bus stop and so Oli told her all about the pink bike and she said, 'Is very good, Oli,' and smiled a big smile. And Oli told the bus driver, only there was a big queue to get on, so he just said, 'Is that right?' and clicked his machine to give them their tickets. So she told the lady sitting behind, and she just laughed because maybe she didn't have many words in her word book either. Mamma said, 'Hush Oli, calm down,' and Pappa wrapped her in his big hug, and they sat together all the way to the High Street.

★

Then they got off the bus and right opposite was the bicycle shop and Oli thought she would just burst with excitement. They went in and there was a funny smell that Pappa said was the rubber tyres on the bikes and the Bicycle Shop Man came out from a back room and said, 'Hello little lady, is it a 25-speed bike you're after?' and Oli said, 'Oh no, I want a pink bike.' And he said, 'Oh, oh dear. I'm afraid we're right out of pink bikes. Would a blue one do?'

Oli didn't know what came over her, because she never did. But it was like the world cracked open and everything that was bad inside came oozing out and Oli began to scream and scream and scream. Mamma tried to hold her and she hit out at her and Pappa picked her up and carried her outside into the sunshine and down the road to the little park where there were swings and slides and he sat on the little swing with her and wouldn't let her go, even though she fought and fought and tried to bite him.

★

After ages, when she had screamed and
screamed and screamed until her voice got
smaller and smaller and smaller, until there
was no scream left, she began to cry, great
big tears. Pappa kept on holding her tight
and Mamma sat on the next swing and they
swung altogether. Then Pappa said, 'C'mon
Oli, let's go feed the ducks, eh?'
So they did and Oli felt very
tired and all empty inside.
Afterwards they went home and
made toastie sandwiches and Oli
opened all her other presents.
Mamma brought in a pink and
white cake with "Happy Birthday
Oli" written on it and Oli blew
out her seven candles and then she fell asleep
on the sofa next to Pappa. She heard the TV
switch on to the football, and Pappa say to
Mamma, 'He said he could get a pink one for
next weekend.'

★

Monday was a bad day at school. Oli didn't like school. The other kids were mostly horrid to her. They wouldn't let her join in their games because she wasn't very good at skipping as she often just couldn't make her arms and legs do what she told them. Anyway, Oli thought she knew much better skipping games but if she got hold of the rope and tried to make them play her way, the other children all just ran away and played hopscotch instead.

But Taylor was nice to her. He was her best friend. The other kids wouldn't let Taylor join in their games either. They said he smelled and

★

his mamma was a psycho and then big tears would roll down his face and the other kids would laugh and run away from him too. He did smell a bit but Oli didn't mind; at her last school, before she came to live with her new mamma and pappa, the other kids used to say that she smelled too. She knew it wasn't Taylor's fault if his clothes weren't very clean. But sometimes she didn't want him to be her friend. She didn't know why, but sometimes she'd push him away when he tried to put his arm round her to comfort her, and once she pushed so hard he fell over and bashed his head. Oli had to see the head teacher and she was so frightened she began to scream, and the head teacher called her mamma to come and take her home.

Taylor

Oli had told everyone she was getting a pink bike for her birthday and she didn't want to tell them what really happened, so she didn't have anything to share at Circle Time.

★

Once she pretended, at her other school, when she was still living with her first mamma. She said at Circle Time that they'd gone to the seaside and her teacher got talking to her first mamma at the gates and her first mamma was so angry when they got home. She said Oli was just trying to show her up as a bad mamma, and then she began to cry and said she was sorry, she was a bad mamma, and would Oli forgive her. That was even worse than when her first mamma shouted that she hated Oli and wished she'd never been born, because Oli didn't want her mamma to be sad and for it to be all her fault.

So when Angela, the nice teaching assistant, said, 'Well Oli, and how was your special day on Saturday?' Oli just looked at the floor and wouldn't say a word. The other kids began to giggle and snigger and Jasmine, who was sitting next to her, whispered, 'Liar, liar, knickers on fire.' So Oli thumped her and Jasmine began to howl and Angela, the nice teaching assistant, said, 'Now Oli, say you're

★

sorry to Jasmine.' Then Oli felt a huge huge rage inside her like a great big bonfire and she opened her mouth and she screamed and screamed and screamed and when the class teacher came in and took hold of her arm and tried to pull her out of Circle Time, Oli bit her.

Then the head teacher called her mamma and her mamma came quickly, and she looked very fed up and sad. The head teacher said, 'Well Mrs Brown, we can't have behaviour like this, it's disrupting the other children,' and Oli's mamma sighed and said, 'Yes, but I've explained about Oli and you're not dealing with it in the right way.' The head teacher fluffed up like a chicken (Oli had seen chickens do that at the City Farm) and said, 'I think I should know how to manage small children. Your child is a MENACE.' Then Oli's mamma took Oli's hand and just said, 'Come on Oli, let's go home,' and they walked really fast out of the office and down the corridor and out into the playground. When they got through the school gates Oli's mamma began to laugh and laugh and laugh

★

and then Oli began to laugh too, and they laughed all the way home.

But when they got home and Oli's pappa came home too, they were very serious and Pappa said to Oli, 'Oli, sweet-pie, you must NOT bite anyone because it hurts, and you wouldn't like to be bitten, would you?' Oli said she was really really sorry about the biting, which she was, but that it wasn't fair that everyone picked on her and, and, and...

Mamma and Pappa

Then they had tea and Oli was very tired after all the screaming, so when Mamma said, 'Time for bed,' Oli was too tired to run away and hide like she usually did at bedtime. She had her bath and got into bed and Pappa came in to read her a story and Oli fell fast asleep.

★

The next day at school Oli wanted to be especially good, but it was numbers and she hated numbers because she couldn't understand how they made different numbers when you piled them on top of each other. So she pinched Taylor and he began to cry, and even Angela, the nice teaching assistant, looked cross and said, 'Oli, please try to be good.' Oli was sorry and tried very hard to be quiet and to listen when the teaching assistant tried to help her with her numbers.

After school Oli asked her mamma if she could go to see Mrs Samski, because she often did, and Mrs Samski would pour her a big glass of

★

milk and give her special biscuits from Poland, which is where Mrs Samski came from and where everyone spoke the strange language Mrs Samski spoke to Mr Samski when he came home with his plumbing tools.

Mamma said, 'Yes, if she'll have you.' So they went downstairs to the floor below and knocked on Mrs Samski's door. Mrs Samski was in and said, 'Come sit, Oli' and she gave her a glass of milk and two Polish biscuits. Oli helped Mrs Samski make Mr Samski's tea, which was dumplings in a big pan of stew, and then she hopped off her stool and said, 'Bye bye, Mrs Samski, I'm going home now.' But when she got to the stairs there were some of the bigger children from the estate hanging round where all the rubbish bins were, and they got all round her and pushed her, and Frankie from the next block said, 'Your mam's not your real mam, you're adopted and your real mam's a druggie and an alkie.'

Mrs. Samski

★

Then they snatched the bag of special Polish sweeties that Mrs Samski had given her for her mamma and ran away, and Oli sat on the bottom step and cried and cried.

Then a voice said, 'Why are you crying, little girl?' Oli wasn't going to stop crying that quickly but she peeped out between her fingers and there was a lady she'd never seen before who was sitting on a big black bicycle. There was a little black dog in the front basket and for a moment Oli thought it was the dog that was talking to her. It had big white teeth and it grinned at her.

Oli was a bit shy but she said, 'The other children were teasing me and they took my sweets.' The lady on the bicycle tutted. 'Just as well,' she said. 'Sweeties are not good for you.'

'But you don't need to cry about it,' she went on, in a quite stern way. So Oli said, 'It's not my fault,' which was what used to make her first mamma even more angry than she had

★

been when she started shouting at Oli. 'Well whose fault is it then?' she'd say. 'What did I do to deserve a bad girl like you? I wish I could send you back and get myself a better daughter.' Even new mamma and pappa sometimes said, 'Oli, it isn't your fault, but it is your responsibility.' But the lady on the bicycle didn't say any of those things. She just said, 'Well, what are you going to do about it?'

Oli said, 'What can I do?' and the lady said, 'We'll work something out together and then you will know what to do about it. But first we have to be introduced.' Oli felt quite grown-up and brave all of a sudden because she, Oli, would know what to do about it (at least she hoped so, but she was used to not knowing what she was supposed to be doing so she didn't worry too much about that). 'What does "introduced" mean?' she asked, because she'd not heard that word before.

'Introduced is when you take me up to your home and you say to your mamma and pappa,

★

"Mamma and Pappa, meet Aggie Witchhazel.
Aggie Witchhazel, meet Mamma and Pappa."
And they say, "How nice to meet you, and how
do you know Oli?" And I say,
"We met on the stairs." Then
we all sit down and have
a cup of tea and become
best of friends.'

And so it was, although
Oli did wonder how Aggie
Witchhazel knew her name
was Oli and why her mamma and pappa didn't
seem surprised to meet Aggie Witchhazel and
she thought maybe, just maybe, they were best
of friends already.

★

So the next day after school, when Oli said to her mamma, 'Can I go and see Aggie Witchhazel?', Oli's mamma said, 'OK, but if she's busy you come straight back.' She watched Oli cross the courtyard, and Oli waved from the walkway outside Aggie's front door, because it turned out Aggie Witchhazel was an opposite neighbour.

Aggie opened the door and told Oli to come right in so Oli didn't think she could have been busy. Her flat wasn't like Oli's. For a start, it had her big black bike in the corridor, which made it hard to squeeze by. The sofa was all lumpy with a hairy blanket thrown over the

★

holes where the stuffing was coming out (Oli peeped under the blanket, which is how she knew about the holes). The little black dog was sleeping on a cushion in one corner of the sofa, so Oli sat in the other.

'We need a strategy,' said Aggie Witchhazel.

'What's a "strattigeegee"?' asked Oli, thinking it might be a bit like a horse, because old Mr Mancini, two doors down, was always saying he was off to "put his shirt on the gee-gees". Pappa told her it meant putting some money on a horse, which sounded a silly thing to do, Oli thought, as it was bound to fall off and get lost or stolen, and sure enough Mr Mancini once told her he'd lost all his money on the gee-gees, but he didn't seem to have learned his lesson.

Aggie tutted and said, 'Concentrate,' as she seemed to know that Oli had gone wandering in her head, which she did quite a lot, and the teachers were always telling her off for daydreaming. But her new mamma always

★

said, 'And how are the fairies today?' and she explained that meant Oli was miles away in her imagination, which was a place in her head that was much bigger than her head could ever be, as big as everywhere and everything and it was her own special world that no one else could come into except if she invited them.

So Oli tried to concentrate really really hard and she scrunched up her forehead until her eyes hurt. And Aggie said, 'Now, I'm going to say three things, and I want you to remember them. I'm going to say, I HAVE, I AM, I CAN. Can you remember that?'

'I HAVE, I AM, I CAN,' said Oli. 'That's easy. But how does that help?'

'It doesn't,' said Aggie. 'Not on its own. It's a sort of special saying – a challenge to yourself. Like the brave deeds that the prince has to do to win the hand of the princess.' Oli made a face; she didn't much rate the princesses waiting in their towers for some weedy prince

★

in tights to rescue them. She'd have tied her
sheets together and climbed down from the
tower and got a life, like new mamma said
when she was reading Oli fairy tales. 'Never
kiss frogs and get a life,' her new mamma said.

'OK,' said Aggie, who seemed to know what Oli
was thinking all the time. 'OK, not princes and
princesses. How about the Big Bad Wolf? You've
got to HUFF and you've
got to PUFF and you've
got to BLOW AWAY ALL
YOUR WORRIES.' The little
black dog leapt to his feet and
barked and Aggie Witchhazel
picked him up and danced with
him round the sitting room.

'So,' said Aggie, a bit breathless, 'How about
we choose three Quests, like in the fairy tales.'

'What's a Quest?' asked Oli.

'A Quest,' said Aggie Witchhazel, 'is a Journey

★

of Discovery.' Oli nodded, to show she understood this was very important. She didn't really, but it sounded fun, like the school magical mystery bus trip to Southend when she'd sat with Taylor and he'd been sick all the way there AND all the way home. That bit wasn't so much fun, of course.

'Your first Quest,' said Aggie Witchhazel, 'is to write me a list of all the people you HAVE in your life who make you feel safe and who care about you and can help you if you're ever in trouble.' She gave Oli a kindly look as though she knew there had been lots of trouble in her life but didn't think any worse of her for that. That she knew all about her first mamma and the uncles who came and went, and the bottles and cans and cigarette ends in Oli's favourite cereal bowl, and about not ever having enough to eat, and being shut in a cupboard in the dark on her own, and not going to school, and sometimes being hit by an uncle and screamed at by her first mamma when she was drunk, and being frightened and cold and very, very

★

alone. It seemed that Aggie Witchhazel knew about before even then: when Oli was just a tiny little bump in her first mamma's tummy and her mamma had drunk too much alcohol and taken bad medicine, so the tiny baby's brain didn't grow quite right. This is what new mamma said when Oli asked her why her legs and arms wouldn't always do what she told them to and she couldn't understand why C A T spelled Mrs Samski's big fluffy Felix and D O G spelled Jango, Taylor's uncle's Pit Bull, when even Taylor knew that, and why it was so hard to remember to listen to her teacher and why the nice teaching assistant Angela had to help her. But she could learn, new mamma said. Oli had all the time in the world to learn.

Then it was Oli's teatime, so she got off the sofa and said goodbye and 'Thank you for having me' to Aggie, who came to the door to watch Oli cross the courtyard to her own staircase. Oli went hop-hop down the stairs, first the left leg, then the right, to be fair to both legs, and then she skipped across the

★

courtyard and went hop-hop upstairs and then she ran along the walkway because she was very hungry now for her tea.

Oli's mamma was making her saucy beans on toast, which is what Oli's pappa called them, and they were her favourite. So Oli sat at the kitchen table with her school exercise book and thought and thought about all the people in her life who loved her and were kind to her and helped her when she was in trouble. She wrote her new mamma and her pappa at the very top of her list. Then she wrote Mrs Samski and Mr Patel at the corner shop, who said 'Milk doesn't grow on trees' when her mamma sent her to buy milk but some kids from the estate stole her money on the way. When Oli said, 'No, Mr Patel, milk grows in cows,' because she was worried that he didn't seem to know, Mr Patel laughed and laughed till he had to wipe his eyes, and Mrs Patel gave her Indian sweeties to take home. Then Oli

Mr Patel

★

wrote down Mrs Jamieson, the school nurse, who was kind to her when she fell over and cut her knee and said she could come and see her anytime she was upset, only Oli was always too upset to remember that when she did get upset. She wrote down Angela, the nice teaching assistant, who helped her with her reading and writing and numbers so that she was getting better at it and sometimes she knew the answer in class. And she wrote down Taylor, who was her best friend even though she didn't have any other less best friends.

Then she felt quite tired with all the thinking and writing and getting the spellings right, but she also felt a bit better. Mamma said, 'Whatever are you writing, Oli?' and Oli said, 'It's a secret list of all my friends' and showed her mamma. And she felt all warm and proud to have such a long list when she didn't think she'd have any names to put on it at all.

★

The next day, after school, Oli told her mamma that she was going to see Aggie Witchhazel and her mamma said, 'Alright, honeydrop, but don't be a nuisance to her and come straight back if she's busy.' Oli hopped down the stairs and skipped across the courtyard (after looking left and right in case the other children were about) and hopped up the stairs to Aggie's flat. Aggie was in, and so was the little black dog, who grinned at Oli with his big white teeth. 'Hastings likes you,' said Aggie Witchhazel, and Oli almost believed

★

her, though she wasn't completely sure. But Hastings sat in his corner of the lumpy sofa and Oli sat in hers, so that was alright.

Aggie said, 'How was your day at school?' and Oli said she'd answered a question in class and got it right, and that Angela, the nice teaching assistant, had been pleased. Aggie said 'Bravo!'

Then Aggie Witchhazel said, 'It's time for your second Quest. I think you should put I AM at the top  of a piece of paper and underneath write a list of all the things that are good about you.' Oli thought this would be really hard, because she wasn't at all sure what was good and what was not and her first mamma always told her what a bad little girl she was even when she was trying her bestest to be good. But Aggie said, 'Don't think about what other people say. Just think about you.' Oli said she would try.

★

So Oli hopped downstairs, left leg first then right leg, to be fair to both legs, and skipped across the courtyard (she thought she saw the other children at the far end but they didn't see her) and hopped upstairs, right leg first then left leg, and then she ran the rest of the way because it was her teatime and she was hungry. Her mamma was working at her computer so Oli sat at the kitchen table with her exercise book and thought and thought and thought. She thought about how she tried to be good and tidy and not be a bother to her new mamma and pappa, though she wasn't always very successful. And she thought about how she always said thank you when Mrs Samski gave her the special Polish sweeties that her cousin brought when she came to stay, and how she helped Mrs Patel fold up the empty cardboard boxes in the shop and put them out for the rubbish lorry. She thought about Taylor, who didn't have any other best friend either and how, when the other kids teased him, she stood up for him and she didn't mind when he sicked up on her on the bus. Not much, anyway.

★

She wrote it all down, very carefully, and then
her mamma came in to make her tea and said,
'What are you writing now, little Oli?' and
Oli said, 'It's my second secret list,' and she
showed her mamma, because she wasn't very
good at keeping secrets. Her mamma gave
her a big kiss on her head and said, 'Tea in
ten,' which is what she always said even if tea
didn't come for a whole half hour.

The next day after school Oli took her list to
Aggie Witchhazel and she said, 'That is such
a good list, Oli.' She showed it to Hastings,
who licked it and looked a bit bored but that
was probably because he had mistaken it for
something to eat, Aggie Witchhazel explained.
Then she said, 'Now Oli, we need to think up
your third and final Quest.' Oli felt quite upset
at the thought that there would be no more
Quests, but she was excited to find out what it
would be too.

'I think your third and final Quest is to write
a list of everything you CAN do to take care

★

of yourself,' said Aggie Witchhazel. This Quest sounded really hard to Oli, because she hadn't ever thought about how to take care of herself. But she said she'd try and she hopped downstairs, and skipped across the courtyard and hopped upstairs, and ran along the walkway and Mamma had got them all a Chinese take-away for tea. So when

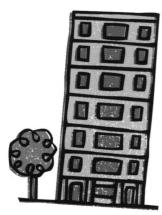

Pappa came home they sat round the table and Oli had a bowl of noodles with bits in it. Mamma told her that Chinese people eat all their food with two little sticks and Oli thought she might get awfully hungry if she had to eat that way and anyway how could she eat her cereal with two sticks?

Then Oli went to her room and got out her exercise book and wrote 'I CAN...' and then she stopped, because she just couldn't think what else to write. So she wrote 'I CAN fly.' But that wasn't right, because she couldn't, so there wasn't any point pretending she could. Then

★

she thought about the nice teaching assistant who told her not to get upset but to think, 'I CAN work it out. HOW can I work it out?' till she found she really could. So she thought, 'I CAN work it out. HOW can I work it out? I know, I'll ask Mamma and Pappa to help me.'

So she picked up her book and pen and went into the sitting room where her mamma and pappa were watching TV. 'Aggie Witchhazel said I was to write a list of all the things I CAN do to take care of me and I don't know what to write,' she told them.

'Good plan,' said Pappa. 'But that is really difficult. Let's all put our heads together and see if we can work this out.' So they sat side by side on the sofa and they thought and thought and thought.

'What can you do when you don't know the answer to the adding up question?' said Mamma.

★

'I can ask Angela, the nice teaching assistant, to explain it to me again,' said Oli.

'Good thinking,' said Pappa. 'Put that down.'

'What can you do when the other children won't let you join in their game?' said Pappa.

'I can say to them that I promise not to be bossy or steal their skipping rope and please would they let me and Taylor play because we feel really sad to be left out,' said Oli, who remembered that was what Mamma had told her to say.

'Excellent plan,' said Mamma. 'Put that down.'

'What can you do when you feel so upset that you just want to run away or hurt yourself or someone else?' said Mamma.

This was a big one, because Oli often felt like that. One time she'd run away into the park, in the dark, and it had been very scary. A man had

★

come after her and she wasn't sure if he was trying to help her or not, but she'd run even faster and it was lucky she'd found the gate again. New Mamma and Pappa had been very cross but only because they'd been so worried, as they explained after the policeman who found her brought her back home. Another time she'd run across the road and a bus had nearly hit her. And there were the times when she thought Taylor was only pretending to be her friend because she was so ugly and wicked he couldn't possibly like her, and then she'd push him away and tell him she never wanted to be his friend ever again, and sometimes he'd cry.

'I don't know,' she said in a very small, sad voice. And Pappa said, 'You can talk to us, Oli. Or Aggie Witchhazel. Talk to all the people on your list of people who care about you. Tell us how we can help. Because we can't do it without you.'

Oli was bursting with happiness because there were all these people who needed her to help

★

them take care of her. She felt bigger and more important than ever before in her whole life.

The next Saturday it wasn't Oli's birthday any more, but Pappa said, 'Any day can be a special Saturday.' So they went on the bus, and when they got off there was the bicycle shop right opposite, and they went in and there was the funny smell of rubber tyres again. Only this time, right in the middle of the shop, there was a pink bicycle and tied to the handlebars was a card with writing in big letters, 'FOR OLI'.

Far, far away Oli thought she heard the ringing of a bicycle bell and the bark of a little black dog. 'I CAN, I HAVE, I AM a little girl with her very own pink bike,' she thought with a smile.

★

Follow THE trail from 1-20 and meet Oli's friends & family on the way to her pink bicycle.

Now that you have finished Oli's story there may be lots of questions that you want to ask. If you have been reading this book with a grown-up, you could go through the qestions that come next and talk about them together.

★

Why do some adults drink too much alcohol and take bad drugs? Isn't it bad for them?

People often start drinking too much alcohol or taking bad drugs to make them feel better when they are sad and upset, but then they get used to them and need more and more and can't stop.

★

How do alcohol and drugs affect babies even before they are born?

Because everything the mother eats and drinks has an effect on how the baby in her tummy grows.

And what happens when those children get older?

They may find it hard to behave well, or they may have difficulties learning or doing PE and playing ball games.

Why isn't it safe for children to live with adults who drink too much alcohol or take drugs?

If parents are drunk on too much alcohol or are high on drugs, they can't look after their children and keep them safe.

Can children like Oli get better? Is there any special medicine that they can take?

There isn't any special medicine, but living in a loving family helps children to get better.

★

What does Aggie Witchhazel's special saying – I HAVE, I AM, I CAN* – mean?

It means that it is always best to think about all the good things you have in your life, like friends and a family, to be proud of who you are, and to know that you can always ask if you need help to do your best.

Why is it important?

Because it is important to feel good about yourself.

Can I HAVE, I AM, I CAN help other children? Should I try to complete Oli's quests?

You could talk it over with someone in your family.

Why is it helpful to share your worries and problems with other people rather than keeping everything to yourself?

Worries are like carrying a heavy sack on

your back. If you share what's in the sack,
it gets lighter and lighter. If you carry it all
by yourself it feels heavier and heavier and
you get worn out.

Why were so many of the other children
in the story horrible to Oli?

Because it is quite hard for children to
accept that it's OK to be different, and they
didn't understand why Oli was different.

Oli has lots of bad memories about her
first mamma. Wouldn't it be better if
she just tried to forget about her?

You can't forget memories just because
you don't like them. It's better to let other
people help you to talk about them and to
remember the good things as well.

How many children have Foetal Alcohol
Syndrome? Is it quite rare?

Some – but not all – children whose
mothers drank too much while they were

★

pregnant may be born with Foetal Alcohol Syndrome. But it is not catching; it isn't like chicken pox!

How would I know if someone in my class has Foetal Alcohol Syndrome?

You probably wouldn't know, but you should always be kind to children who seem a little different or less able than you are yourself.

How could I help them?

Always try to be helpful to all children who have difficulties with learning, with games and with making friends. Think how they might be feeling and let them join in!

*The model of I HAVE, I AM, I CAN was developed by Dr Edith Grotberg and the International Resilience Project. See Edith H Grotberg (ed.) Resilience for today: gaining strength from adversity. Westport CT: Prager Publishers; 2003. See also guidance published by Alcohol Concern in the UK for its Parenting & Alcohol Project, available from the SCIE Social Care Online resource library at http://www.scie-socialcareonline.org.uk/profile.asp?guid=9f78b460-c50f-404f-b317-9075c68e9939

★